FIRST FRENCH WORDS

Premiers Mots Anglais

Note for Adults
This book is intended for parents and other adults who speak at least a little French themselves and who would like their children to begin to enjoy discovering French too. The book contains a story with a dual language text which introduces young children to the sounds and cadences of a foreign language. In every scene, from kitchen to bedroom to park, everyday objects are clearly labelled in French and in English, enabling even quite small children to enjoy identifying and learning some French words. Additional sections introduce children to the words for numbers, colours and parts of the body. Your child will find learning some French with Topsy and Tim great fun!

The book includes a comprehensive index for adult use. Please note that the two story texts are idiomatic rather than literal translations.

Précision pour les Adultes
Ce livre est destiné aux parents et autres adultes parlant au moins un peu anglais et désireux de voir leurs enfants se réjouir d'une première découverte de cette langue. Le livre contient une histoire avec un texte en deux langues, ce qui fait connaître aux jeunes enfants les sons et les cadences d'une langue étrangère. Dans chaque scène, de la cuisine à la chambre à coucher, jusqu'au parc, chaque objet est désigné en anglais et en français, permettant, même aux petits enfants, de s'amuser à identifier et à apprendre quelques mots anglais. Une partie supplémentaire introduit les nombres anglais ainsi que les couleurs et les parties du corps. Votre enfant va trouver très amusant d'apprendre un peu d'anglais avec Topsy et Tim.

Le livre comprend un index complet à l'intention des adultes. Nous vous faisons remarquer que la traduction de l'histoire est plus idiomatique que littérale.

BLACKIE CHILDREN'S BOOKS

Published by the Penguin Group
Penguin Books Ltd, 27 Wrights Lane, London W8 5TZ, England
Penguin Books USA Inc., 375 Hudson Street, New York, New York 10014, USA
Penguin Books Australia Ltd, Ringwood, Victoria, Australia
Penguin Books Canada Ltd, 10 Alcorn Avenue, Toronto, Ontario, Canada M4V 3B2
Penguin Books (NZ) Ltd, 182–190 Wairau Road, Auckland 10, New Zealand

Penguin Books Ltd, Registered Offices: Harmondsworth, Middlesex, England

Text originally published as *Topsy and Tim Word Book* © 1984 Jean & Gareth Adamson
This edition first published 1995 by Blackie Children's Books
10 9 8 7 6 5 4 3 2 1

Text translated by Donald Nicholson-Smith

Design by Between the Lines, London
Filmset in Century Schoolbook Infant
Made and printed in China by Imago

A CIP catalogue record for this book is available from the British Library

ISBN 0-216-940915 Hbk
ISBN 0-216-94092-3 Pbk

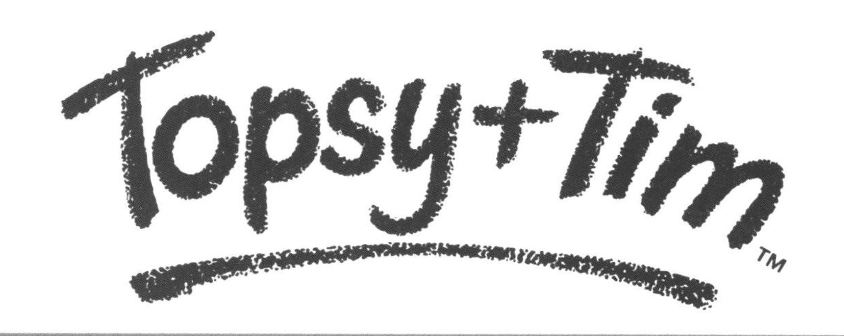

FIRST FRENCH WORDS

Premiers Mots Anglais

Jean and Gareth Adamson

Blackie Children's Books

Topsy and Tim are getting ready to go out. They are going to buy a birthday present for Josie Miller.

Topsy et Tim se préparent à sortir. Ils vont acheter un cadeau d'anniversaire pour Josie Miller.

carrier bag
le sac en plastique

coat
le manteau
hat
le chapeau
scarf
l'écharpe
umbrella
le parapluie
buttons
les boutons
dress
la robe
handbag
le sac à main
wellingtons
les bottes en caoutchouc
bobble hat
le bonnet
anorak
l'anorak
belt
la ceinture
jumper
le pull
T-shirt
le teeshirt
pocket
la poche
skirt
la jupe
jeans
le jean
tights
le collant
socks
les chaussettes
laces
les lacets
shoes
les chaussures
trainers
les baskets

Mummy takes them to a toyshop to choose a present for Josie. They choose a jigsaw puzzle.

Maman les emmène chez un marchand de jouets pour choisir le cadeau de Josie. Ils choisissent un puzzle.

paintbox
la boîte de peinture

puppets
les marionnettes

rocking horse
le cheval à bascule

doll's house
la maison de poupée

darts set
le jeu de fléchettes
roller skates
les patins à roulettes
guitar
la guitare
doll
la poupée
computer
l'ordinateur
dinosaur
le dinosaure
helicopter
l'hélicoptère
video game
le jeu vidéo
tricycle
le tricycle
bricks
les cubes
jigsaw
le puzzle
marbles
les billes
space ship
le vaisseau spatial

On the way home Topsy and Tim go to the supermarket, where they help Mummy to do her own shopping.

Avant de rentrer, Topsy et Tim accompagnent leur mère au supermarché. Ils l'aident à faire ses achats.

purse
le porte-monnaie
till
la caisse
basket
le panier
money
l'argent
meat
la viande
bread
le pain
cake
le gâteau
milk
le lait
orange
l'orange
lemon
le citron
biscuits
les petits gâteaux
carrots
les carottes
bananas
les bananes
apples
les pommes
lettuce
la laitue
potatoes
les pommes de terre
tomatoes
les tomates

When they get home Topsy and Tim make birthday cards for Josie. Topsy wraps the jigsaw puzzle in pretty paper and ties it with yellow ribbon.

De retour à la maison, Topsy et Tim fabriquent des cartes d'anniversaire pour Josie. Topsy emballe le puzzle dans un joli papier, et met un ruban jaune autour.

wrapping paper
le papier cadeau

water
l'eau
pair of scissors
la paire de ciseaux
rubber
la gomme
ribbon
le ruban
parcel
le paquet
pencil
le crayon
poster paints
les gouaches
birthday card
la carte d'anniversaire
table
la table
crayons
les pastels
ruler
la règle

Topsy does not want much lunch.

'We are saving lots of room for Josie's birthday cake,' says Topsy.

'And ice-cream too,' adds Tim.

Topsy ne veut pas beaucoup manger à midi.

'Nous gardons beaucoup de place pour le gâteau d'anniversaire de Josie,' dit Topsy.

'Et pour la glace aussi,' ajoute Tim.

teapot
la théière

plate
l'assiette
saucers
les soucoupes
jug
le pichet
cup
la tasse
window
la fenêtre
eggcup
le coquetier
fridge
le frigo
sink
l'évier
peas
les petits pois
spoon
la cuiller
knife
le couteau
fork
la fourchette
stool
le tabouret
chair
la chaise
kitchen table
la table de cuisine

Topsy and Tim play in their garden until it is time to get ready for Josie's birthday party.

'Try not to get too dirty,' calls Mummy.

Topsy et Tim jouent dans le jardin en attendant l'heure de se préparer pour aller à l'anniversaire de Josie.

'Essayez de ne pas trop vous salir,' crie Maman.

watering can
l'arrosoir

trousers
le pantalon
lawn
la pelouse
bike
le vélo
shears
la cisaille
butterfly
le papillon
wheelbarrow
la brouette
hutch
le clapier
bee
l'abeille
daisies
les pâquerettes
rabbit
le lapin
lawnmower
la tondeuse à gazon
snail
l'escargot
forget-me-nots
les myosotis

At last they are washed, dressed and on their way. They take a short cut through the park.

Les voilà enfin propres, habillés et prêts à partir. Ils prennent un raccourci à travers le parc.

refreshment stand
la buvette

kite
le cerf-volant
girl
la fille
boy
le garçon
sand pit
le bac à sable
scooter
la trottinette
slide
le tobogan
man
l'homme
buggy
la poussette
lake
le lac
duckling
le caneton
flowers
les fleurs

Josie is waiting for them.

'Hurry up, Topsy and Tim,' she calls. 'The party has already begun.'

Josie les attend.

'Dépêchez-vous, Topsy et Tim,' lance-t-elle. 'La fête est déjà commencée.'

car
la voiture

butcher's shop
la boucherie
grocer's shop
l'épicerie
book shop
la librairie
smoke
la fumée
chimney
la cheminée
lamp post
le réverbère
roof
le toit
front door
la porte d'entrée
pavement
le trottoir
hedge
la haie

The party tea is scrumptious. Tim eats so much ice-cream that he has no room for birthday cake.

'Never mind,' says Josie. 'You can take a piece home with you.'

Il y a des tas de choses délicieuses à manger. Tim mange tant de glace qu'il ne lui reste plus de place pour le gâteau d'anniversaire.

'Ça ne fait rien,' dit Josie. 'Tu peux toujours en emporter une part.'

paper hat
le chapeau en papier

paper chains
les guirlandes de papier
birthday cake
le gâteau d'anniversaire
sandwiches
les sandwichs
orange juice
le jus d'orange
tablecloth
la nappe
straws
les pailles
glass
le verre
potato crisps
les chips
napkins
les serviettes de table
fizzy drinks
les boissons gazeuses

When the party is over Dad takes Topsy and Tim home.

'I can see you had a good time,' said Mummy.

Après la fête c'est Papa qui ramène Topsy et Tim à la maison.

'Je vois que vous vous êtes bien amusés,' dit Maman.

aquarium
l'aquarium

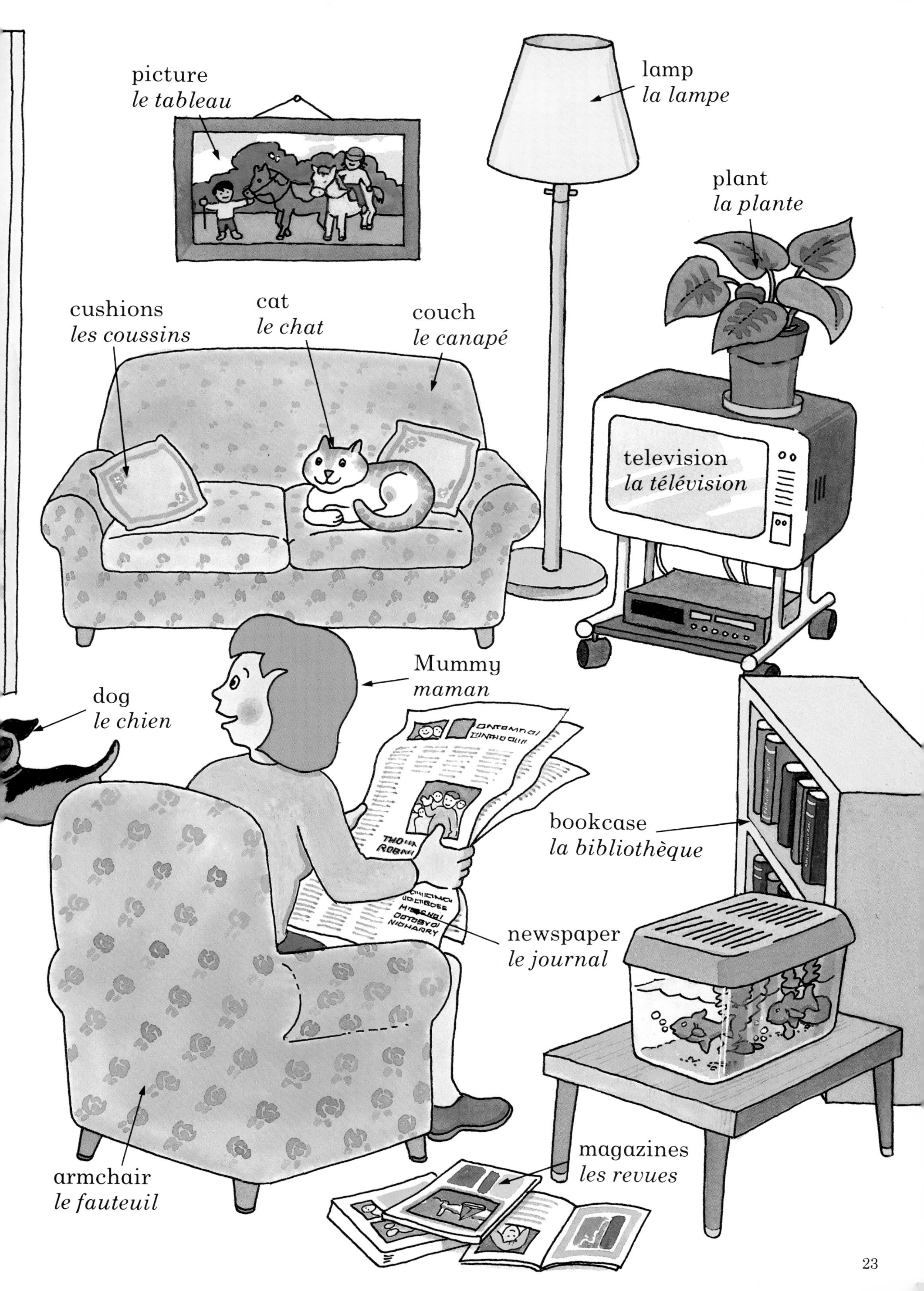
picture
le tableau
lamp
la lampe
plant
la plante
cushions
les coussins
cat
le chat
couch
le canapé
television
la télévision
Mummy
maman
dog
le chien
bookcase
la bibliothèque
newspaper
le journal
magazines
les revues
armchair
le fauteuil

Topsy and Tim play with their party balloons in the bath. Tim's balloon comes undone and whizzes all round the bathroom.

Dans le bain Topsy et Tim jouent avec les ballons qu'ils ont rapportés. Le ballon de Tim perd sa ficelle et s'envole dans la salle de bain.

toothbrushes
les brosses à dents

shower
la douche
tiles
les carreaux
mirror
le miroir
plug
la bonde
washbasin
le lavabo
toothpaste
le dentifrice
pyjamas
le pyjama
bathmat
le tapis de bain
toilet
les toilettes
towel
la serviette

'Did Josie like her jigsaw puzzle?' asks Mummy, as she tucks them into bed.
'She got three,' says Topsy. 'But she likes ours best.'

*'Est-ce que le puzzle a plu à Josie?' demande Maman en les mettant au lit.
'Elle en a reçu trois,' dit Topsy, 'mais c'est le nôtre qu'elle préfère.'*

slippers
les pantoufles

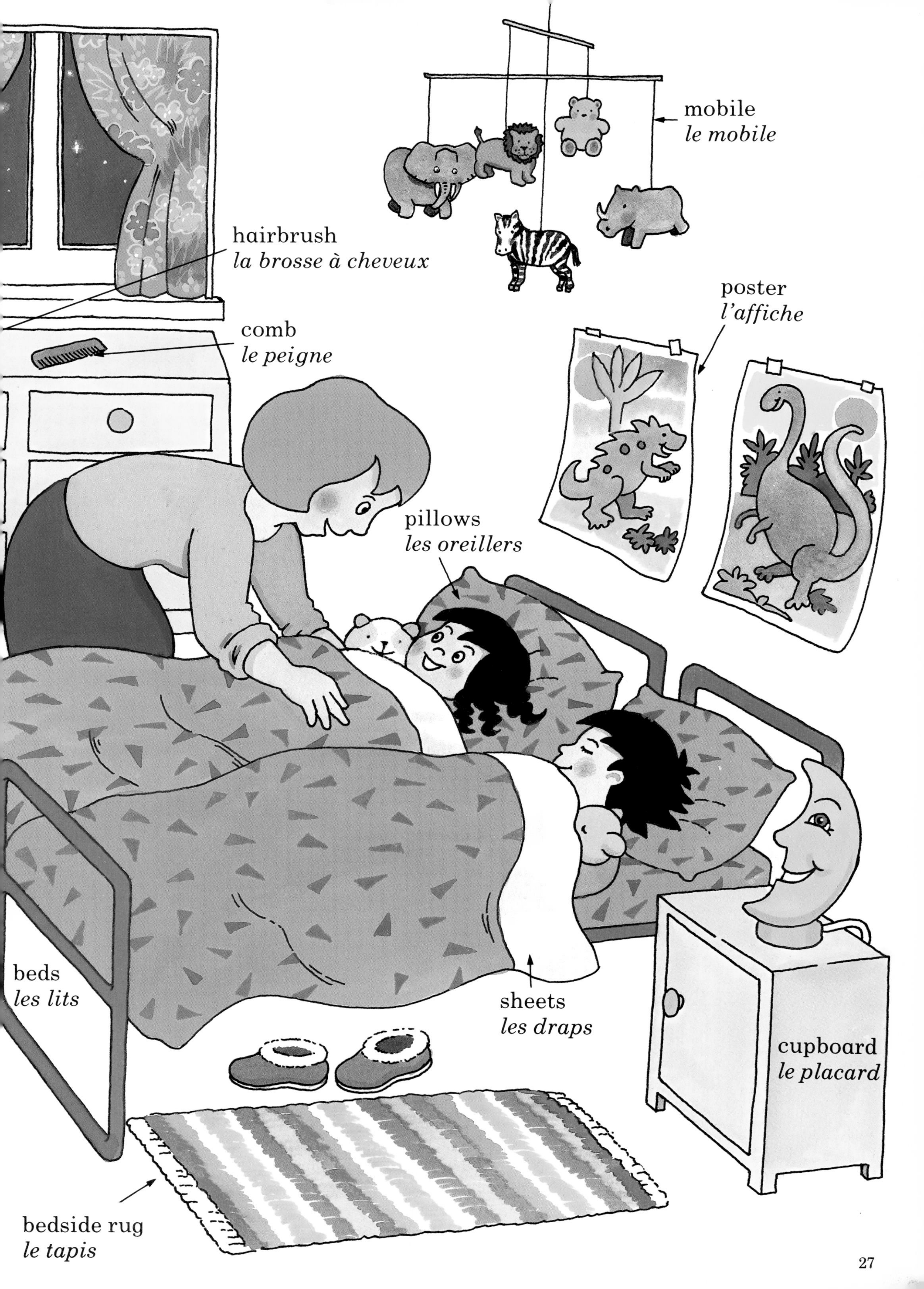
mobile
le mobile
hairbrush
la brosse à cheveux
poster
l'affiche
comb
le peigne
pillows
les oreillers
beds
les lits
sheets
les draps
cupboard
le placard
bedside rug
le tapis

PARTS
OF THE
BODY
LES PARTIES
DU CORPS
head
la tête
teeth
les dents
thumb
le pouce
cheek
la joue
arm
le bras
elbow
le coude
stomach
le ventre
fingers
les doigts
hair
les cheveux
eye
l'oeil
legs
les jambes
nose
le nez
ears
les oreilles
mouth
la bouche
chin
le menton
toes
les doigts de pied
shoulders
les épaules
tail
la queue
tongue
la langue
bottom
le derrière
hand
la main
knee
le genou
paws
les pattes
feet
les pieds

COLOURS *LES COULEURS*

NUMBERS *LES NOMBRES*

one	two	three	four	five
1	2	3	4	5
un	*deux*	*trois*	*quatre*	*cinq*

six	seven	eight	nine	ten
6	7	8	9	10
six	*sept*	*huit*	*neuf*	*dix*

ENGLISH/*FRENCH*

to add/*ajouter* 12
anorak/*l'anorak* (m) 5
apple/*la pomme* 9
aquarium/*l'aquarium* (m) 22
arm/*le bras* 28
armchair/*le fauteuil* 23
to ask/*demander* 26

baby/*le bébé* 16
balloon/*le ballon* 20
banana/*la banane* 9
basket/*le panier* 9
bath-tub/*la baignoire* 24
bath/*le bain* 24
bathmat/*le tapis de bain* 25
bathroom/*la salle de bain* 24
bed/*le lit* 26, 27
bedside rug/*le tapis* 27
bee/*l'abeille* (f) 15
to begin/*commencer* 18
belt/*la ceinture* 5
bench/*le banc* 16
bike/*le vélo* 14
bird/*l'oiseau* (m) 14
birthday cake/
le gâteau d'anniversaire 12, 20, 21
birthday card/
la carte d'anniversaire 10, 11, 20
birthday present/
le cadeau d'anniversaire 20
black/*noir* 29
blue/*bleu* 29
bobble hat/*le bonnet* 5
book shop/*la librairie* 19
bookcase/*la bibliothèque* 23
bottom/*le derrière* 28
boy/*le garçon* 17
bread/*le pain* 9
brick/*le cube* 7
to bring back/*ramener* 22
brother/*le frère* 22
brown/*marron* 29
buggy/*la poussette* 17
bus/*l'autobus* (m) 18
butcher's shop/*la boucherie* 19
butter/*le beurre* 8
butterfly/*le papillon* 15
button/*le bouton* 5
to buy/*acheter* 4

cake/*le gâteau* 9
car/*la voiture* 18
carrier bag/*le sac en plastique* 4
carrot/*la carotte* 9
cat/*le chat* 23
chair/*la chaise* 13
cheek/*la joue* 28
cheese/*le fromage* 8
chest of drawers/*la commode* 26
chimney/*la cheminée* 19
chin/*le menton* 28
to choose/*choisir* 6
clock/*la pendule* 12
coat/*le manteau* 5
coffee/*le café* 8
comb/*le peigne* 27
computer/*l'ordinateur* (m) 7
cooker/*la cuisinière* 12
couch/*le canapé* 23
crayon/*le pastel* 11
cup/*la tasse* 13
cupboard/*le placard* 12, 27
cushion/*le coussin* 23
Dad/*papa* (m) 22
daisy/*la pâquerette* 15
darts/*le jeu de fléchettes* 7
dinosaur/*le dinosaure* 7
dog/*le chien* 22
doll/*la poupée* 7
doll's house/*la maison de poupée* 6
door/*la porte* 22
dress/*la robe* 5
duck/*le canard* 16
duckling/*le caneton* 17

ear/*l'oreille* (f) 28
to eat/*manger* 20
egg/*l'oeuf* (m) 8
egg cup/*le coquetier* 13
eight/*huit* 29
elbow/*le coude* 28
exercise book/*le cahier* 26
eye/*l'oeil* (m) 28

felt-tipped pen/*le feutre* 10
finger/ *le doigt* 28
fish/*le poisson* 9
fizzy drink/*la boisson gazeuse* 21
five/*cinq* 29
flour/*la farine* 8
flower/*la fleur* 17
to fly away/*s'envoler* 24
foot/*le pied* 28
forget-me-not/*le myosotis* 15
fork/*la fourchette* 13
four/*quatre* 29
fridge/*le frigo* 13
front door/*la porte d'entrée* 19
fruit/*le fruit* 8

garage/*le garage* 18
garden/*le jardin* 14
to get dirty/*se salir* 14
gift/*le cadeau* 20
girl/*la fille* 17
glass/*le verre* 21
to go out/*sortir* 4
green/*vert* 29
grey/*gris* 29
grocer's shop/*l'épicerie* (f) 19
guitar/*la guitare* 7

hair/*les cheveux* (m) 28
hairbrush/*la brosse à cheveux* 27
hand/*la main* 28
handbag/*le sac à main* 5
hat/*le chapeau* 5
head/*la tête* 28
heater/*l'appareil de chauffage* (m) 22
hedge/*la haie* 19
helicopter/*l'hélicoptère* (m) 7
to help/*aider* 8
house/*la maison* 10
hutch/*le clapier* 15

ice-cream/*la glace* 12, 20

jam/*la confiture* 8
jeans/*le jean* 5
jigsaw puzzle/*le puzzle* 6, 7, 26
jug/*le pichet* 13
jumper/*le pull* 5

kettle/*la bouilloire* 12
kitchen table/*la table de cuisine* 13
kite/*le cerf-volant* 17
knee/*le genou* 28
knife/*le couteau* 13

lace/*le lacet* 5
lake/*le lac* 17
lamp/*la lampe* 23
lamp post/*le réverbère* 19
lawn/*la pelouse* 15
lawnmower/*la tondeuse à gazon* 15
leg/*la jambe* 28
lemon/*le citron* 9
lettuce/*la laitue* 9
litterbin/*la boîte à ordures* 16

magazine/*la revue* 23
to make/*fabriquer* 10
man/*l'homme* (m) 17
marble/*la bille* 7
meat/*la viande* 9
milk/*le lait* 9
mirror/*le miroir* 25
mobile/*le mobile* 27
money/*l'argent* (m) 9
mother/*la mère* 8
motorbike/*la moto* 18
mouth/*la bouche* 28
Mummy/*maman* (f) 6, 14, 22, 26

napkin/*la serviette de table* 21
newspaper/*le journal* 23
nine/*neuf* 29
nose/*le nez* 28

one/*un* (m) *une* (f) 29
orange/*orange* 29
orange/*l'orange* (f) 9
orange juice/*le jus d'orange* 21

paintbox/*la boîte de peinture* 6
paintbrush/*le pinceau* 10
painting/*la peinture* 10
pair of scissors/*la paire de ciseaux* 11
paper chain/*la guirlande de papier* 21
paper hat/*le chapeau en papier* 20
parcel/*le paquet* 11
park/*le parc* 16
party/*la fête* 18, 22
pavement/*le trottoir* 19
paw/*la patte* 28
pea/*le petit pois* 13
phone box/*la cabine téléphonique* 18
picture/*le tableau* 23
pink/*rose* 29
plant/*la plante* 23
plate/*l'assiette* (f) 13
to play/*jouer* 14, 24
plug/*la bonde* 25
pocket/*la poche* 5
post office/*la poste* 18
poster/*l'affiche* (f) 27
poster paint/*la gouache* 11
potato/*la pomme de terre* 9
potato crisp/*le chip* 21
to prepare/*préparer* 4
present/*le cadeau* 4
puppet/*la marionnette* 6
purse/*le porte-monnaie* 9
to put on/*mettre* 10
pyjamas/*le pyjama* 25

rabbit/*le lapin* 15
radio/*la radio* 20
rake/*le râteau* 14
red/*rouge* 29
refreshment stand/*la buvette* 16
ribbon/*le ruban* 10, 11

rocking horse/*le cheval à bascule* 6
roller skate/*le patin à roulettes* 7
roof/*le toit* 19
rubber/*la gomme* 11
ruler/*la règle* 11

sand pit/*le bac à sable* 17
sandwich/*le sandwich* 21
saucepan/*la casserole* 12
saucer/*la soucoupe* 13
sausage/la *saucisse* 12
to save/*garder* 12
to say/*dire* 12
scarf/*l'écharpe* (f) 5
school bag/*le cartable* 26
scooter/*la trottinette* 17
to see/*voir* 22
seven/*sept* 29
shampoo/*le shampooing* 24
shears/*la cisaille* 15
sheet/*le drap* 27
shoe/*la chaussure* 5
short cut/*le raccourci* 16
shoulder/*l'epaule* (f) 28
shower/*la douche* 25
sink/*l'évier* (m) 13
sister/*la soeur* 22
six/*six* 29
skateboard/*la planche à roulettes* 16
skipping rope/*la corde à sauter* 16
skirt/*la jupe* 5
slide/*le tobogan* 17
slipper/*la pantoufle* 26
smoke/*la fumée* 19
snail/*l'escargot* (m) 15
soap/*le savon* 24
sock/*la chaussette* 5
space ship/*le vaisseau spatial* 7
spade/*la bêche* 14
sponge/*l'éponge* (f) 24
spoon/*la cuiller* 13
stomach/*le ventre* 28
stool/*le tabouret* 13
straw/*la paille* 21
sugar/*le sucre* 8
supermarket/*le supermarché* 8
sweet/*le bonbon* 8
swing/*la balançoire* 14

T-shirt/*le teeshirt* 5
table/*la table* 11
tablecloth/*la nappe* 21
tail/*la queue* 28
to take/*prendre* 15
to take away/*emmener* 6
to take away/*emporter* 20
tea/*le thé* 8
teapot/*la théière* 12
telephone/*le téléphone* 22
television/*la télévision* 23
ten/*dix* 29
tennis racquet/*la raquette de tennis* 26
three/*trois* 29
thumb/*le pouce* 28
tights/*le collant* 5
tile/*le carreau* 25
till/*la caisse* 9
toe/*le doigt de pied* 28
toilet/*les toilettes* (f) 25
tomato/*la tomate* 9
tongue/*la langue* 28
tooth/*la dent* 28
toothbrush/*la brosse à dents* 24
toothpaste/*le dentifrice* 25
towel/*la serviette* 25
toyseller/*le marchand de jouets* 6
traffic lights/*les feux* (m) 18
trainers/*les baskets* (m) 5
tree/*l'arbre* (m) 16
tricycle/*le tricycle* 7
trolley/*le chariot* 8
trousers/*le pantalon* 15
to try/*essayer* 14
two/*deux* 29

umbrella/*le parapluie* 5

video game/*le jeu vidéo* 7

to wait/*attendre* 18
to want/*vouloir* 12
wardrobe/*l'armoire* (f) 26
washbasin/*le lavabo* 25
water/*l'eau* (f) 11
watering can/*l'arrosoir* (m) 14
wellington boot/
la botte en caoutchouc 5
wheelbarrow/*la brouette* 15
white/*blanc* 29
window/*la fenêtre* 13
woman/*la femme* 17
to wrap/*emballer* 10
wrapping paper/*le papier cadeau* 10

yellow/*jaune* 29
yoghurt/*le yaourt* 8

zebra crossing/*le passage clouté* 18

FRENCH/ENGLISH

l'abeille (f)/bee 15
acheter/to buy 4
l'affiche (f)/poster 27
aider/to help 8
ajouter/to add 12
l'anorak (m)/anorak 5
l'appareil de chauffage (m)/heater 22
l'aquarium (m)/aquarium 22
l'arbre (m)/tree 16
l'argent (m)/money 9
l'armoire (f)/wardrobe 26
l'arrosoir (m)/watering can 14
l'assiette (f)/plate 13
attendre/to wait 18
l'autobus (m)/bus 18

le bac à sable/sand pit 17
la baignoire/bath-tub 24
le bain/bath 24
la balançoire/swing 14
le ballon/ballon 20
la banane/banana 9
le banc/bench 16
les baskets (m)/trainers 5
le bébé/baby 16
la bêche/spade 14
le beurre/butter 8
la bibliothèque/book case 23
la bille/marble 7
blanc/white 29
bleu/blue 29
la boisson gazeuse/fizzy drink 21
la boîte à ordures/litter bin 16
la boîte de peinture/paintbox 6
le bonbon/sweet 8
la bonde/plug 25
le bonnet/bobble hat 5
la botte en caoutchouc/
wellington boot 5
la bouche/mouth 28
la boucherie/butcher's shop 19
la bouilloire/kettle 12
le bouton/button 5
le bras/arm 28
la brosse à cheveux/hairbrush 27
la brosse à dents/toothbrush 24
la brouette/wheelbarrow 15
la buvette/refreshment stand 16

la cabine téléphonique/phone box 18
le cadeau/gift 20
le cadeau/present 4
le cadeau d'anniversaire/
birthday present 20
le café/coffee 8
le cahier/exercise book 26
la caisse/till 9
le canapé/couch 23
le canard/duck 16
le caneton/duckling 17
le carreau/tile 25
la carotte/carrot 9
le cartable/school bag 26
la carte d'anniversaire/
birthday card 10, 11, 20
la casserole/saucepan 12
la ceinture/belt 5
le cerf-volant/kite 17
la chaise/chair 13
le chapeau/hat 5
le chapeau en papier/paper hat 20
le chariot/trolley 8
le chat/cat 23
la chaussette/sock 5
la chaussure/shoe 5
la cheminée/chimney 19
le cheval à bascule/rocking horse 6
les cheveux (m)/hair 28
le chien/dog 22
le chip/potato crisp 21
choisir/to choose 6
cinq/five 29
la cisaille/shears 15
le citron/lemon 9
le clapier/hutch 15
le collant/tights 5
commencer/to begin 18
la commode/chest of drawers 26
la confiture/jam 8
le coquetier/eggcup 13
la corde à sauter/skipping rope 16
le coude/elbow 28
le coussin/cushion 23
le couteau/knife 13
le cube/brick 7
la cuiller/spoon 13
la cuisinière/cooker 12

demander/to ask 26
la dent/tooth 28
le dentifrice/toothpaste 25
le derrière/bottom 28
deux/two 29
le dinosaure/dinosaur 7
dire/to say 12
dix/ten 29
le doigt/finger 28
le doigt de pied/toe 28

la douche/shower 25
le drap/sheet 27

l'eau (f)/water 11
l'écharpe (f)/scarf 5
emballer/to wrap 10
emmener/to take away 6
emporter/to take away 20
s'envoler/to fly away 24
l'épaule (f)/shoulder 28
l'épicerie (f)/grocer's shop 19
l'éponge (f)/sponge 24
l'escargot (m)/snail 15
essayer/to try 14
l'évier (m)/sink 13

fabriquer/to make 10
la farine/flour 8
le fauteuil/armchair 23
la femme/woman 17
la fenêtre/window 13
la fête/party 18, 22
le feutre/felt-tipped pen 10
les feux (m)/ traffic lights 18
la fille/girl 17
la fleur/flower 17
la fourchette/fork 13
le frère/brother 22
le frigo/fridge 13
le fromage/cheese 8
le fruit/fruit 8
la fumée/smoke 19

le garage/garage 18
le garçon/boy 17
garder/to save 12
le gâteau/cake 9
le gâteau d'anniversaire/
birthday cake 12, 20, 21
le genou/knee 28
la glace/ice-cream 12, 20
la gomme/rubber 11
la gouache/poster paint 11
gris/grey 29
la guirlande de papier/paper chain 21
la guitare/guitar 7

la haie/hedge 19
l'hélicoptère (m)/helicopter 7
l'homme (m)/man 17
huit/eight 29

la jambe/leg 28
le jardin/garden 14
jaune/yellow 29
le jean/jeans 5
le jeu de fléchettes/darts set 7
le jeu vidéo/video game 7
la joue/cheek 28
jouer/to play 14, 24
le journal/newspaper 23
la jupe/skirt 5
le jus d'orange/orange juice 21

le lac/lake 17
le lacet/lace 5
le lait/milk 9
la laitue/lettuce 9
la lampe/lamp 23
la langue/tongue 28
le lapin/rabbit 15
le lavabo/washbasin 25
la librairie/book shop 19
le lit/bed 26, 27

la main/hand 28
la maison/house 10
la maison de poupée/doll's house 6
maman (f)/Mummy 6, 14, 22, 26
manger/to eat 20
le manteau/ coat 5
le marchand de jouets/toy seller 6
la marionnette/puppet 6
marron/brown 29
le menton/chin 28
la mère/mother 8
mettre/to put on 10
le miroir/mirror 25
le mobile/mobile 27
la moto/motorbike 18
le myosotis/forget-me-not 15

la nappe/tablecloth 21
neuf/nine 29
le nez/nose 28
noir/black 29

l'oeil (m)/eye 28
l'oeuf (m)/egg 8
orange/orange 29
l'orange (f)/orange 9
l'ordinateur (m)/computer 7
l'oreille (f)/ear 28
l'oreiller (m)/pillow 27
l'oiseau (m)/bird 14

la paille/straw 21
le pain/bread 9
la paire de ciseaux/pair of scissors 11
le panier/basket 9
le pantalon/trousers 15
la pantoufle/slipper 26
papa (m)/Dad 22
le papier cadeau/wrapping paper 10
le papillon/butterfly 15
la pâquerette/daisy 15
le paquet/parcel 11
le parapluie/umbrella 5
le parc/park 16
le passage clouté/zebra crossing 18
le pastel/crayon 11
le patin à roulettes/roller skate 7
la patte/paw 28
le peigne/comb 27
la peinture/painting 10
la pelouse/lawn 15
la pendule/clock 12
le petit pois/pea 13
le pichet/jug 13
le pied/foot 28
le pinceau/paintbrush 10
le placard/cupboard 12, 27
la planche à roulettes/skateboard 16
la plante/plant 23
la poche/pocket 5
le poisson/fish 9
la pomme/apple 9
la pomme de terre/potato 9
la porte/door 22
la porte d'entrée/front door 19
le porte-monnaie/purse 9
la poste/post office 18
le pouce/thumb 28
la poupée/doll 7
la poussette/buggy 17
prende/to take 16
préparer/to prepare 4
le pull/jumper 5
le puzzle/jigsaw puzzle 6, 7, 26
le pyjama/pyjamas 25

quatre/four 29
la queue/tail 28

le raccourci/short cut 16
la radio/radio 20
ramener/to bring back 22
la raquette de tennis/tennis racquet 26
le râteau/rake 14
la règle/ruler 11
le réverbère/lamp post 19
la revue/magazine 23
la robe/dress 5
rose/pink 29
rouge/red 29
le ruban/ribbon 10, 11

le sac à main/handbag 5
le sac en plastique/carrier bag 4
se salir/to get dirty 14
le sandwich/sandwich 21
le saucisse/sausage 12
le savon/soap 24
sept/seven 29
la serviette/towel 25
la serviette de table/napkin 21
le shampooing/shampoo 24
six/six 29
la soeur/sister 22
sortir/to go out 4
la soucoupe/saucer 13
le sucre/sugar 8
le supermarché/supermarket 8

la table/table 11
la table de cuisine/kitchen table 13
le tableau/picture 23
le tabouret/stool 13
le tapis/bedside rug 27
le tapis de bain/bathmat 25
la tasse/cup 13
le teeshirt/T-shirt 5
le téléphone/telephone 22
la télévision/television 23
la tête/head 28
le thé/tea 8
la théière/teapot 12
le tobogan/slide 17
les toilettes (f)/toilet 25
le toit/roof 19
la tomate/tomato 9
la tondeuse à gazon/lawnmower 15
le tricycle/tricycle 7
trois/three 29
la trottinette/scooter 17
le trottoir/pavement 19

un (m) *une* (f)/one 29

le vaisseau spatial/space ship 7
le vélo/bike 14
le ventre/stomach 28
le verre/glass 21
vert/green 29
la viande/meat 9
voir/to see 22
la voiture/car 18
vouloir/to want 12

le yaourt/yoghurt 8